I Don't Want To

Julia Donaldson
Illustrated by Karen Donnelly

RIGBY

"Hi, Lily!" said Tim.

"Let's climb my tree."

But Lily said, "No, I don't want to."

"Let's play in my den," said Tim.

But Lily said, "No, I don't want to."

"Do you want to ride my bike?"
asked Tim.

"No," said Lily. "I don't want to."

"Do you want to go on my swing?"
asked Tim.

"No," said Lily. "I don't want to."

Lily said, "I don't like your swing.
I don't like your bike.
I don't like your den or your tree.
I don't want to play in your garden."

Then Tim saw Ali.

"Hi, Tim!" called Ali.

"Let's climb your tree!"

So Tim and Ali climbed
the tree.

They played in the den.

Tim had a ride on the bike.
Ali had a go on the swing.

Then they saw Lily.

"Hi, Tim! Hi, Ali!" she called.

"Can I play, too?"